THE CAREGIVER COFFEEBREAK

**Take a Break
Before You Break:
76 Practical Tips
To Help Caregivers**

Carry On!

Bret

BY
BREEDA MILLER

©2017 by Breeda Miller

Visit **BreedaMiller.com**

Published by Soar2Success Publishing
Visit **Soar2Success.com**

ISBN: 9781943043361

Printed in the USA

Book Design by Chris Mendoza
ChrisdMendoza.com

TABLE OF CONTENTS

DEDICATION:

This book is dedicated to my brightest star — my dear mother,
Mary Kelly. She taught me everything I know about being a
caregiver. She gave care and received care more graciously
than anyone I've ever known. Her spirit lives on in many
ways and she has inspired me to help other caregivers
carry on. Never at a loss for words or wisdom,
Mary Kelly continues to light the way for us all.

A Note from Breeda

Caregiving is not for sissies. It's a messy business and a lonely one at that. I spent years caring for my dear mother and I often felt I was the only one dealing with the frustration, exhaustion and isolation of caregiving. I decided to become a Caregiver Champion because I learned so many life lessons during those years and I hope to share those lessons with you. One of the most important is to remember to take care of yourself, to *Take a Break, Before You Break.* That's how the Caregiver Coffeebreak was born. It's a soft spot, a safe space to take a moment, catch your breath and find a way to refresh yourself. Whether you spend a few minutes with this book or watch a Caregiver Coffeebreak video, I hope you will feel supported, inspired or maybe even amused. As a caregiver we should take our work seriously, but never ourselves. My motto is, "Blessed are the flexible, for they shall not get bent out of shape." Take good care — of yourself!

Breeda Miller

SELF-CARE IS NOT SELFISH

Take a Break Before You Break

Giving yourself permission to take a break is a huge step in taking care of yourself. When I was a child I remember my mother used to take a break every day to watch her soap opera, *As the World Turns*. She called it her "story." She made herself a cup of tea and sat down to watch this half hour program. Then she got up and went back to cooking, cleaning, ironing and caring for five children.

Our lives today are different. We are always on the go with to-do lists longer than Santa's. But it's not noble to be a run down, exhausted and cranky caregiver. You will feel better, be more effective and be a happier person when you take care of yourself. Figure out what works for you and make sure you take time for yourself, every day.

SELF-CARE IS NOT SELFISH

Lower Your Standards

It is not possible to have an immaculate house, a perfect wardrobe, a well-stocked pantry, well-adjusted children, a fascinating career, a great relationship and be an effective caregiver. I honestly don't think it's possible to have three of those things at the same time.

We imagine that everybody else is doing life better than we are. We think other caregivers never lose their cool, prepare better meals, manage their household cheerfully and are perfect parents, spouses, sons and daughters. It's a lie. The truth is that we need to pick our priorities and do what needs to be done at that moment. Adjust your life to your circumstances. One day you will have the time and energy to clean the baseboards and repaint the living room. Until then, don't feel guilty about all the things that you could be doing. Take care of yourself.

SELF-CARE IS NOT SELFISH

Tea for One

Pour yourself a cuppa. Whether it's tea or coffee (or even an occasional adult beverage), find a cozy spot to enjoy a few minutes with a cup or a mug.

My mother believed a hot cup of tea cured just about everything.

It's soothing and you just can't drink it fast. Take a moment and find that spot on the porch, in a nice chair, in a bedroom, or if you have to, go in the basement.

Create a little oasis for yourself and focus on enjoying that singular cup of comfort. An intentional short break can do more good than you can ever imagine.

SELF-CARE IS NOT SELFISH

Furry Friends to the Rescue

A treat I often give myself is a visit to the local animal shelter.
I have two rescue dogs and I love them dearly, so I'm not looking
for a new family member. But I like to stop in to
visit the dogs waiting for families.

I take time at each cage to make eye contact and speak gently to them.
I tell them that they will be going to a new home soon (it's a no-kill
shelter) and I try to give them a bit of encouragement.

I leave the shelter feeling that I gave comfort to animals and gave
myself a moment to appreciate all that I have in my life.

SELF-CARE IS NOT SELFISH

Talk to Yourself

We believe what we tell ourselves. Self-talk is powerful and can be transformative. If you are constantly putting yourself down with phrases like, "I'm such a bad daughter" or "I am so bad at taking care of mom" or "I hate my life," it's even harder to do all that you need to do as a caregiver.

Be gentle with yourself and choose kind words. Catch yourself when you are being negative and flip it around. "I'm doing the best that I can. I am here." "I'm learning how to take care of mom." "This is a really hard time in my life and I am doing my best. It won't last forever."

You can't control the circumstances, but you can control your reactions and how you talk to yourself.

SELF-CARE IS NOT SELFISH

One Goal: Have a Good Day

Realistic expectations can make a huge difference in how we deal
with difficult times. Instead of focusing on a cure or getting
better or stronger (which may not be possible), just plan to
Have a Good Day, whatever that looks like to you.

Maybe it's eliminating a bad behavior or de-cluttering one drawer or
watching a funny video. Maybe it's sharing a good memory or
making a call to an old friend. Small actions add up.
Try to make those actions as positive as possible.

SELF-CARE IS NOT SELFISH

Minimize Toxic Exposure

Toxic people can suck the life out of you. Whether they are clueless family members or unreliable friends who cause stress by not following through on promises to help, it can be toxic and detrimental to your health. Don't engage in the drama. That's why we have Netflix. You can find plenty of drama there and you can turn it off when you've had enough.

Be polite but firm. Find ways to minimize your exposure to toxic people if you can't eliminate them from your life. At the very least, consider the source whenever they say something unkind.

Don't give them the power to upset you.
You are doing the best you can.

SELF-CARE IS NOT SELFISH

Be Like Elsa — Let It Go!

Guilt. Let it go. It's not helpful and it can exhaust you quicker than changing bedding four times a day. If you are doing everything you can to take good care of your person and you feel guilty that you are not doing enough, you are wasting precious time and energy.

You cannot cure Alzheimer's Disease or other dementias. You can only do the best of your abilities on any given day. Some days will be better than others. Cherish those days and remember what a good job you are doing. On the bad days, forgive yourself and know that you will do better tomorrow.

Then, Let It Go.

SELF-CARE IS NOT SELFISH

Find Your People

Find an experience that has nothing to do with caregiving — something just for you. Your library might have a book club or a group for knitters. Your church might assemble care packages; maybe a local bakery has a bread baking class. I loved being involved in community theater while I cared for my mom. It was an 8-week commitment and there were weekly rehearsals and plenty of opportunity for volunteers to help out, even if they weren't interested in being on stage. I could go to rehearsal and immerse myself for three hours into another world with different people. It had nothing to do with my family – it was just for me. It was fun and it had an end date (the final performance). Some folks painted scenery, some worked on the costumes, some helped sell tickets. I looked forward to my rehearsal time and it helped to sustain me. What type of social group would provide you with a break?

SELF-CARE IS NOT SELFISH

10

Forty Winks

What's your nap-ability? Some people have the ability to take a nap and feel recharged and refreshed. Some folks feel guilty and lazy if they take a nap. I am fortunate to be able to take a 20-minute nap and feel like a new person. I used to feel very guilty about a midday nap, but now I consider it a highly desirable talent. I know when I keep pushing myself to the point of exhaustion that the quality of my work suffers, my interaction with people is not pleasant (just ask my children) and my ability to focus rivals that of a gnat. Get a soft sleep mask, find a quiet spot and just sink into the couch or chair. Close your eyes and focus on your breathing. Try to relax your tongue. Even if you don't actually fall asleep, that short bit of rest may be enough to restore you to carry on.

SELF-CARE IS NOT SELFISH

You Can't Pour from an Empty Cup

If ever there was a visual regarding the importance of self-care, it's an empty cup. You may have the best of intentions, but you are human and you have limitations. You need to take care of yourself so that you can care for others. It's as simple (and as difficult) as that.

Self-care means different things to different people. It's not about getting massages and pedicures (though those are wonderful). It's about knowing your limits, finding ways to recharge, keeping your sense of humor, staying healthy and being kind to yourself. Caregiving is not a competition, in spite of what your sister might think.

Self-Care is not Selfish

One a Day — One a Week — One a Month

I'm not talking about the vitamins here but a special list of things or activities that you can plan and look forward to.

Some examples: a warm bath, a 15-minute walk, a cup of rich cocoa, a movie, a trip to the library, a drive to a local attraction, a visit to a nearby city, lunch at a favorite restaurant, treasure hunting at a thrift shop, an exercise class, a massage, or reading a trashy novel for half an hour.

Give yourself a gift of a pleasant experience. These can be planned and anticipated or spontaneous. Either way, doing so will help make you a better caregiver instead of a bitter caregiver.

SELF-CARE IS NOT SELFISH

Write it Down

The people in our care are not the only ones who forget things. When something funny happens or you feel really frustrated – write it down. Keep a notebook and jot down when mom says something outrageous or dad tells a great story about his early years. Take a few moments to vent and write down your feelings of frustration or anger. It's amazing how just the act of writing it down helps diffuse the negative emotions and feeling of helplessness. Don't share it with anyone unless it would be helpful. Keeping a journal that has both the good and bad experiences will free up your brain to be in the moment. You will be able to look back on your experiences when you are no longer a caregiver. Don't feel you have to share this with anyone else. Privacy can be very freeing. Check out the *Caregiver Calming Coloring Journal*. It's two stress reducers in one portable book available at **BreedaMiller.com**.

SELF-CARE IS NOT SELFISH

Take a Walk

Even if you can't go far, just putting on walking shoes and going around the block can make a positive difference. It can be a great way to start your day, but you might not have that kind of flexibility in your morning. So, try to plan a time every day, maybe mid-morning or after lunch, to take a 5 or 10 minute walk.

You will clear your head, calm yourself down and know you are doing something very good for yourself. You might like it so much that you will build up your time to take longer walks, but don't push yourself at first. Just get out there and go. I like to listen to audio books when I walk and find I walk farther if the book is good and I want to hear the end of a chapter.

SELF-CARE IS NOT SELFISH

Color My World

There is something very soothing and mindless about coloring. It's all the rage now and it's fun to see the variety of coloring books available. I've seen fancy high-art coloring books and wickedly funny "adult" ones as well. Markers, pencils and pens are great, but there is nothing like cracking open a big, fresh 64-count box of Crayola® crayons. I have no intention of framing or keeping my "masterpieces" so I don't worry about my color choices or even try to plan them. I just start coloring and give my brain a little break. It feels very therapeutic. Check out my *Caregiver Calming Coloring Journal.* It is a small notebook filled with lined pages for notes and coloring pages when you want to relax, or can't figure out what to write. It's also easy to take with you to doctor's visits. It keeps you occupied in waiting rooms, and it's also a great place to take notes from the doctor. **BreedaMiller.com/Coloring-Journal**

SELF-CARE IS NOT SELFISH

Massage Magic

I never had a massage until I became a caregiver. There, I said it. I was always self-conscious about this mysterious experience. I was embarrassed and didn't know where to go or what would actually happen behind the closed door.

When my stress level reached a number that Richter didn't even register, I decided to be brave and make an appointment. My neck felt like there were knives permanently embedded between my shoulders due to the stress.

Needless to say, the massage was pure bliss. I decided that I needed to do this at least every month just to keep my sanity. It was a $25 luxury that became a necessity and it was magical.

I highly recommend massages. They're also a great gift idea for caregivers.

SELF-CARE IS NOT SELFISH

Breath of Life

Deep breathing is a great stress reducer.

When I am about to go into a stressful situation like a meeting with difficult people, or just thinking about a challenging situation, I pause and focus on my breathing.

I take a deep breath and hold it for a count of four, then exhale for a count of four. Then I repeat that cycle at least three more times.

I imagine a square and each breath in and out completes one line of the square. Whether it's the conscious pause, the actual deep breathing and increased oxygen in my system, or all of the above, it helps me deal with tough situations. My breathing is the one thing I know I can control.

SELF-CARE IS NOT SELFISH

18

Love Your Library

Local libraries are a caregiver's best friend.

A library is a nearby oasis where you can go to sit and read
a magazine, check out traditional or audio books,
use a computer and browse the internet.

Borrow movies, music and TV shows. Some libraries have an amazing
array of items to borrow — from tools to sporting equipment.

I like them because they are local and nearby, so you
don't need to factor in travel time when you are able
to get out of the house on your own.

Best of all, there is no cost, unless you
forget to return the items, of course!

SELF-CARE IS NOT SELFISH

Indulge Yourself

Martyrs aren't fun, and being a caregiver doesn't require you
to become one. Find ways to feel good, enjoy life,
and indulge in pleasurable activities.

Maybe taking a twenty minute bubble bath with a
luxurious bath product would be a special treat.

A nap can be delicious as long as you don't lie awake
feeling guilty about taking a nap during the day.

A square or two of high-quality chocolate
may have medicinal properties.

A nice glass of wine can be intoxicating in many ways.

While at the market, pick up some fresh flowers to brighten
your table. Go ahead, indulge yourself. You deserve it.

SELF-CARE IS NOT SELFISH

20

Mental Bingo

Mind games are one of the best ways to deal with difficult people and difficult situations. I play Mental Bingo daily. In my mind I have a giant Bingo card. At the top I have five categories (or more!) filled with the words or behaviors that absolutely drive me crazy.

I know that certain individuals will say certain things or behave in a certain way that will totally push my buttons. Instead of reacting in a negative way and giving them the power to annoy me, I turn it around. I anticipate and expect them to say or do things that bug me. Then, when they come through, instead of being annoyed, I say to myself, "Bingo!"

I can't control them, but I can control how I respond to them. Try it and see if you feel empowered by a little mind game. Just don't tell the other person you are playing.

SELF-CARE IS NOT SELFISH

Pick One Thing

Stress is a killer.

Don't get stressed out trying to do all the things suggested just to try and minimize your stress!

Pick one thing and try it.

See how it feels and if it works for you.

Remember, you have choices and options. Practicing self-care strategies is the most important thing you can do to reduce stress.

SELF-CARE IS NOT SELFISH

Reality of Fatigue

People don't often recognize sleep deprivation in themselves. Moderate sleep deprivation can produce impairments in your abilities equal to a blood alcohol level of .10 — all the bad consequences without any of the fun.

Sleep deprived people experience changes in brain chemistry that make them crave higher calorie foods and reduces their ability to resist temptation.

Don't let that happen to you.

Take a nap, go to bed, and work on finding creative ways to rest. If you're exhausted because a loved one is in constant motion and never seems to sleep, make arrangements for someone to stay with them so you can sleep.

SELF-CARE IS NOT SELFISH

Sleep Tips

Inadequate sleep will greatly increase your levels of stress and irritability. Here are some great tips to aid in restful sleep and better tomorrows:

- Skip the snooze button. Those extra few minutes really don't provide additional rest. Figure out the realistic time you need to get up and out of bed, and then set your alarm for that time.

- Avoid eating 2-3 hours before sleep onset. It's harder for your body to wind down when it's busy digesting food.

- Use caffeine wisely (remember: soda and tea can contain caffeine).

- Take a warm bath or shower before bed to help you relax.

- Room darkening shades can help in the summer months.

- Splurge on good sheets. They're a luxury that you will enjoy every night.

SELF-CARE IS NOT SELFISH

Enjoy Anti-Stress Foods

Here are a few great foods that help decrease stress levels.

Fruits, Vegetables, & Berries: Avocado, Leafy Greens, and Blueberries

Nuts & Seeds: Pistachio, Pumpkin, Sesame, and Sunflower

Meats: Turkey and Salmon

Treats: Dark Chocolate (!)

Keep them handy as snacks and find creative ways to include them in your meals. Have some already portioned out in snack bags so you can take them with you on the go.

Also, don't forget to take your vitamins –
you need all the strength and energy you can get!

SELF-CARE IS NOT SELFISH

Calm App

Calm is the #1 app for mindfulness and meditation.

The app helps you lessen anxiety and get better sleep through guided meditation, sleep stories, breathing programs and relaxing music.

It's perfect for beginners and it's free. The app will ask you to subscribe, just decline and you can still access great free content.

For intermediate and advanced users, there are many additional programs available within the app.

SELF-CARE IS NOT SELFISH

26

Three Things

Each night before you go to sleep, think through the day and choose
three good things that happened or that went well.

It can be something small, like the absence of bad things.
It can be an ordinary thing like having a meal with
your loved one that he or she was able to enjoy.

No matter how big or small the good things are, write them down.
As you write them down, you will go to bed focusing on positive things,
which will help to retrain your brain to consistently remember the
good in life, no matter how bad the day may have been.

Memory is a tricky thing but you can outthink it. Keep
a notebook next to your bed and get in the habit of
writing down your three things every night.

SELF-CARE IS NOT SELFISH

Farm it Out

You can't do everything. Figure out what you are good at and what you like doing. Enlist help from family members or hire people who can help do the things that are at the bottom of your list. Many times people offer to help and caregivers brush them away because it seems like more trouble to explain things and organize them than to just do it themselves. Or perhaps you feel that no one else could do things just the way you do them and that won't work for you. Please let it go and allow others to help. Maybe it's paying the bills, picking up prescriptions, or doing a regular stop at the market for weekly items. Your place of worship or senior center may have volunteers looking for ways to help out. Allow them to help you.

Here is a template you can download to help you sort it out:
<u>BreedaMiller.com/downloads</u>

SELF-CARE IS NOT SELFISH

Talk it Out

Sometimes a professional is the only one who can help you manage yourself when you feel overwhelmed and exhausted.

At one point in caring for my mother, I knew I was going over the edge.

I asked for a referral from our hospice social worker and she recommended a local therapist. I only saw him five times (that's what our insurance covered) but those sessions did me a world of good.

I gained wisdom as well as an outside perspective. It was a very kind and supportive experience that really helped me get through a very difficult time.

CLEVER IDEAS

GUBS

Grown Up Bibs = GUBS

Caring for a person with Parkinson's Disease or other illnesses that cause tremors and shaking can make mealtimes very messy. My friend created funny and imaginative bibs from a large towel. They were decorated as different characters — Batman, Superman, Wonder Woman, Tuxedo, Playboy Bunny — you get the idea.

Here's the cool part: They were stored in a drawer and when the family sat down for dinner, all four chose the GUB they wanted to wear. Her dad was never embarrassed about wearing a bib because everyone wore one. It was a fun way to begin a meal and saved a lot of messes at the same time
AdultBibsWithAttitude.com

CLEVER IDEAS

Disposable Underwear

Only people under age three wear diapers. Everyone else who needs them wears disposable underwear. Calling them diapers is not helpful and only makes people feel embarrassed and diminished.

Apart from saving your furniture and too frequent bedding changes, disposable underwear can be a lifesaver. Studies have shown that adults at risk for falling have fewer falls if they wear disposable underwear. The reason is that due to fear of falling, many seniors wait until the last second to get to the bathroom and might feel panicked and hurry. By wearing disposable underwear, there is no longer a sense of urgency because if there is a leak, it's not a problem. Less stress, less mess, fewer falls.

For more information, check out this video at
BreedaMiller.com/video.

CLEVER IDEAS

IKEA® Cutlery

Modern cutlery can be oversized and heavy. Arthritic hands can have a hard time managing big forks and heavy knives.

The OXO® Good Grips are great, but they can be pricey, especially if someone loads them incorrectly in the dishwasher and they melt. Just sayin'.

IKEA sells an entire set of plastic cutlery (meant for kids). Kalas: 18 pieces for $2.49. They are very comfortable to hold, they cut meat, and are attractive as well. They also have a nice selection of small matching cups and bowls that are good portion sizes for small eaters.

IKEA.com/us/en/catalog/products/90192962/#

CLEVER IDEAS

32

Diaper Genie®

Disposable underwear is wonderful until you have to actually dispose of it in the same room. A good friend told me that simply putting the items in the wastebasket in her mother's room at the care home was a big problem.

To eliminate the problem, she brought in a product meant for nurseries, the *Diaper Genie*. She uses it to dispose of the odorous items and said she can't believe the difference it has made.

Now her mom's room smells lovely!

CLEVER IDEAS

Adult Sippy Cups

Lids on cups are fabulous!

There are so many types to choose from, whether your loved one prefers a straw, or drinking straight from the special lid. Choose a style that is easy to manage and make sure the lid is secure.

Avoid the tricky ones that require coordination to open with your hand when you want to take a sip. Even if the opening remains open, spilling will be much less than a cup without any type of lid.

CLEVER IDEAS

Wheelchair as Fashion

The decision to use a wheelchair was a big one. Mom was mobile but moved at glacier speed even with her walker. If we were going to be able to go out and about, we needed to find a wheelchair that worked for our needs. It was a challenge to find one that she would agree to use and one that I could lift into my car.

I found a transport wheelchair online that was pretty! It had a plaid pattern and my mother loved it. I found a scarf that matched (sort of) and whenever we went out, people commented on her beautiful wheelchair. She was very proud and never resisted using her new fashionable mode of transport.

Drivemedical.com/index.php/fly-lite-aluminum-transport-chair-948.html

CLEVER IDEAS

Car Trips — In and Out Made Easier

Transferring my mom from her transit wheelchair into my car was
a real challenge. Her clothing would stick to the fabric of the
car seat and she couldn't lift her bottom to scoot over.

An Occupational Therapist suggested we keep a new garbage bag in
the car on the seat. Then, when helping her get in and out of
the car, she just slid right into place. It worked like a charm.

As a bonus, if there were any messes in the car,
we had a plastic bag ready!

CLEVER IDEAS

36

Caregiver Tool Kit

If you are new to caregiving, you may not be aware of a
variety of items available that can make your ability
to care for your loved one much easier.

Download this list, separated into two parts:
one is for safety, and the other is for daily care.

You may not need all these items at this time, but down the
road they can make all the difference to you and your loved one.

<u>BreedaMiller.com/downloads</u>

CLEVER IDEAS

Quick Meal Idea

Family dinners often didn't suit my mother's palate.

Pizza and tacos were too spicy or hard to eat.

My go-to quick meal was a baked potato (microwaved),
a small portion of meat (ham, chicken or sautéed
ground meat) and a portion of vegetables.

Nutritious, simple and easy. It's hard having to prepare a
separate meal, but if you know what your loved one is
able to eat and you have it ready to go, there
is much less stress for everyone at mealtime.

The best advice is to just keep it simple.

CLEVER IDEAS

38

Fidget Blanket

People with dementia often feel the need to keep busy and without something to occupy their hands they can become quite anxious.

Have a stash of options ready to go to help avoid destructive behaviors.

Etsy is a website that has a wide selection of handmade items to consider. You can buy them or find inspiration on how to make your own.

Fidget blankets and aprons are a great way to provide a distraction that keeps hands busy, and you don't have to worry about the "fidget items" getting misplaced or ingested because they are sewn onto the fabric.

Find your inspiration at **Etsy.com.**

CLEVER IDEAS

A Job

Everyone needs a sense of purpose. When you offer a helpful job to your loved one, everyone will be happier, healthier and ready to sleep at night. My mom helped me by feeding my paper shredder. I gave her a box full of papers and she fed the machine one paper at a time. Doing dishes and wiping down counters might be something that your loved one enjoys and is able to do. Keep a stack of small hand towels that need to be folded. Smoothing out tissue paper or crumpled newspapers is another job to consider. One woman told her bedridden dad that a company wanted to hire him to pop bubble wrap and would pay him for each roll completely popped. He worked at it all day and she did a quality inspection each evening. He enjoyed his job and she told him "the company" said he was their best employee and would get a raise. He was happy, busy, and felt he had a purpose.

CLEVER IDEAS

40

Weighted Blankets

Many people find that a therapeutic weighted
blanket helps them sleep better at night.

For those folks, a weighted blanket is comforting and relieves anxiety.
There are many sources for these blankets and you can decide which
level of weight you want, based on body weight.

Amazon.com

CLEVER IDEAS

Puzzles that Don't Frustrate

You can download and print free large-print crossword puzzles and word searches. Traditional jigsaw puzzles have too many pieces for seniors with dementia, so look for puzzles that have images that are appealing to adults (not childish) and offer a variety of levels of difficulty.

From as few pieces as 12 up to 500, the larger the pieces are, the easier they are to pick up and place. Puzzles are a great activity to engage several generations at a time. A designated folding table makes this an easy ready-to-go activity, as well as a great diversion for loved ones when needed.

Qets.com/crossword_puzzles.htm

Jigsawpuzzlesforadults.com/jigsaw-puzzles-for-seniors

CLEVER IDEAS

Aging in Place

Never underestimate the value of a first floor bathroom, ideally a full bathroom. You can modify a study or dining room into a temporary first floor bedroom fairly easily. But without a first floor bathroom, many loved ones have no option but to move out or into assisted living.

Whether it's for an elderly family member or someone with a newly replaced hip or knee, a first floor bathroom can make all the difference in the world.

In addition, a portable commode can help with distance issues (getting to the bathroom) or can serve as an assist if placed over the traditional toilet. The seat is elevated and the hand rails make it easier to get up and down.

CLEVER IDEAS

Hi-Tech Sanity Saver

The Amazon Echo, Google Home, and other forms of Smart Assistance Devices offer a break from repetitive questions to caregivers.

What day is it? What time is it? What's the weather going to be like today? Can you turn on some music? How do you spell Thursday? These smart devices can answer a wide variety of questions, play simple games, tell stories and jokes, or give you the news of the day.

There's so much that can be handled by this amazing piece of technology. The cost is under $200 and it could be a wonderful gift for a special caregiver in your life.

CLEVER IDEAS

Silly Bin

Target and your local Dollar Store are great resources for stocking your Silly Bin. Keep a box filled with fun and quirky toys, props, or items that your loved one might enjoy.

When you need a diversion to deal with boredom or agitation, these items might save the day. Magic wands, crowns, yo-yos, kazoos, stuffed animals, and wind-up toys can offer a few minutes of fun and be a welcomed distraction for you and your loved one.

CLEVER IDEAS

Digital Family Legacy

A digital family legacy can be a treasure of photos, documents and data.
It can also be a therapeutic activity to build while caring for a frail loved
one. As the only daughter, I was the keeper of precious family photos
and documents. I knew more stories about our family than my brothers
did and while I sat with my mother in her room, I worked on this
family book on my laptop. I had family photos scanned and cleaned,
I checked with cousins in other countries about names and dates.
I wrote down the little stories I grew up hearing, even if they weren't
flattering to everyone involved. They were our family truths. I used a
free site to do all this and when it was done I could order as few copies
as I wanted and family members could go online and read the book
without having to order it at all. As a bonus, whenever a
niece or nephew gets married I have a present ready to go!

Visit **Blurb.com**.

CLEVER IDEAS

Nasty Noise

You can't control everything, but whenever you can
eliminate harsh sounds and noises you should do it.

Does your phone's ring tone annoy you? Find something that
catches your attention but is pleasant to hear. I downloaded
the Harry Potter theme from iTunes ($1.49) and it
gives me a little smile whenever I hear it.

Is your alarm a rude buzzer? Change it to something more pleasant and
start your day a little gentler. Just be sure it's loud enough to do the job.

CLEVER IDEAS

Fabulous Field Trips

Be a tourist in your own town. Create a list of places to visit and sites to see. Figure out which ones are accessible, within a good driving distance, and interesting to you and your loved one.

A local art museum had a Norman Rockwell exhibit and with our snazzy new transport wheelchair we had a lovely day enjoying the art. Many beaches have wheelchair accessible boardwalks. Riverwalks in cities are now common.

Is there a local tourist spot that visitors travel to your area to see? It may have been years since you have been and even longer for your loved one.

Make a date and find a way to get out of the house.

GOLDEN RESOURCES

Area Agency on Aging

Your area has a dedicated agency designed to help you find
resources and assistance from local resources.

Contact the *National Association of Area Agencies on Aging*
to find the nearest *Agency on Aging* serving you.

This should be your first stop for support as a family caregiver.

Visit **N4A.org**.

GOLDEN RESOURCES

Alzheimer's Association

This organization raises money to help fund research through a variety of activities all across the United States.

They also provide support groups, resources, educational events and more for families affected by Alzheimer's Disease.

Go to **Alz.org**.

GOLDEN RESOURCES

Cruising Through Caregiving

If you read only one book to help you as a caregiver (besides this one), I recommend Jennifer FitzPatrick's comprehensive and easy to digest new book, *Cruising Through Caregiving*. Jennifer covers all the bases and answers questions you might never have considered.

She lays out options and resources as well as coping strategies for dealing with uncooperative siblings, determining the type and level of care your loved one needs, how to navigate the senior health care system and most importantly, how to take care of yourself as you navigate these challenging waters.

CruisingThroughCaregiving.com

GOLDEN RESOURCES

Passages in Caregiving

Author Gail Sheehy wrote a great book called *Passages in Caregiving* in 2010. She outlined her challenges as a caregiver and her research into the factors that allow some caregivers to become ill and lose years from their lifespan and others who manage to find the caregiving role as one of the most uplifting and ultimately positive experiences in their lifetime.

Of course, many folks have experiences that are in the middle with plenty of ups and downs. Sheehy's style of research, analysis and her own experiences provide a really useful resource for caregivers.

GOLDEN RESOURCES

Hospice Care

Hospice is an umbrella term, not a specific organization. There are for-profit and non-profit hospice organizations. Like anything, there are great ones, good ones, and not-so-good ones. Ask your friends, family and medical professionals for their recommendations and check them out. Hospice is so often misunderstood and called in too late to really help. The goal of hospice care is to provide comfort care, rather than finding a cure. In many cases, Medicare covers the cost of hospice care. I know that hospice saved my life when I cared for my mother and she enjoyed a much greater quality of life because of the care provided by hospice.

National Hospice & Palliative Care Organization:
NHPCO.org/find-hospice
National Association for Home Care and Hospice: **NAHC.org**
Hospice Foundation of America: **HospiceFoundation.org**

GOLDEN RESOURCES

AARP

Sure, you can get great discounts and the magazine now features rock stars on the cover, but AARP offers a treasure trove of resources for aging well as well as for caregivers of older adults.

If you are new to caregiving, check out the Basics menu selection, and look for the *Prepare to Care* section on their website for valuable information and downloads.

Visit **AARP.org/caregiving.**

GOLDEN RESOURCES

PACE

The National PACE Association serves communities across the U.S., providing services designed to keep seniors independent and living in their own homes.

Services include Clinic and Day Health Centers, Medical Specialists, Transportation Services, Family/Caregiver Support Services, Rehab and Durable Goods, Medical Equipment, Medicare, and Medicaid Services.

Services are limited to the participating counties/ regions listed on the PACE website.

Visit **www.Pace4You.org** or call **1-800-MEDICARE.**

GOLDEN RESOURCES

When You Don't Know What You Don't Know

There are many professionals who can help you sort out the dizzying array of options, forms and laws that impact your responsibilities as a caregiver. While it may cost you a few hundred dollars for their advice and counsel, their expertise can potentially save you thousands of dollars and years of heartache.

- Eldercare lawyers specialize in laws impacting seniors. Visit **lcplfa.org.**

- Aging Life Care Managers are specialized nurses / social workers that offer advice and help with creating care plans. Visit **aginglifecare.org.**

- Social Workers specialize in a variety of areas related to elder care like Medicare management, hospice care, and bereavement support.

Also visit: *Everything Mediation* at **Mediate.com**

National Elder Law Foundation at **NELF.org**

State Health Insurance Assistance Programs at **SHIPTAcenter.org**

GOLDEN RESOURCES

Medicare 101

It can be overwhelming. Not only are you physically and mentally exhausted from caring for your loved one, but also you have to figure out how to get help and how to pay for it. There is a big difference between Medicare and Medicaid.

Also, there are variations of Medicare. To understand Medicare and insurance options and see how they apply to your situation, check out the FREE assistance from the State Health Insurance Assistance Program (SHIP) through your local Area Agency on Aging. Plug in your zip code on these two websites to find out who is nearby to help you.

Visit the Area Agency on Aging at **N4A.org** and SHIP at **SHIPTAcenter.org**.

GOLDEN RESOURCES

57

Help from the VA

Elderly veterans may be eligible for a wide variety of benefits available to all U.S. military veterans. VA benefits include disability compensation, pension, education and training, health care, home loans, insurance, vocational rehabilitation and employment, and burial.

Follow the link to the Veterans page for an overview of the benefits available to all veterans. Widows and widowers of veterans may also be able to find support for senior care.

Benefits.va.gov/persona/veteran-elderly.asp

Social Insecurity

Social Security and Social Security Disability often require the patience of a saint to navigate when it comes to obtaining benefits. There are terms to know and income levels to be mindful of, especially if you are caring for a disabled individual who has a part-time job.

Being the Payee means you receive the disability check and are responsible for disbursing funds to care for the person receiving the payment. Best advice is to seek the counsel of an expert Social Security lawyer in your area. Your Area Council on Aging can help you find one.

Visit **N4A.org**.

GOLDEN RESOURCES

The Conversation

Talking about the end of life is something that most people want to avoid. However, if you want to know exactly what your loved one's preferences are, you need to have this conversation. While my mother was still active and healthy, she told me (in no uncertain terms) exactly what she wanted, even down to which hymns to sing and who should sing them! She even made me go with her to pick out a cemetery plot so she could be sure of a "good view" and good neighbors. It was such a gift. When she died, I didn't have to make major decisions and get into any discussions or arguments about what we should do. It was a wonderful last gift of love from her. Don't wait until death is imminent; have the conversation when it seems like a distant future event. That will make it easier and could even become an empowering time of creativity. For help on this, visit **TheConversationProject.org**.

GOLDEN RESOURCES

60

DailyCaring.com

This free website curates tips and articles from a wide variety
of sources and has great archives available to you so you
can research past articles and posts.

In addition to their website, they have a daily newsletter that provides
new information right in your email box every day.

DailyCaring.com

GOLDEN RESOURCES

Senior Services

You can't do it alone. Whether it's a community based service like a local senior center or funded programs like Meals on Wheels or a commercial home care service, help is available.

You may be able to find help from a member of the local senior group or a volunteer from your church who is looking for a little extra spending money by being a companion for your loved one (for a short time), so you can *Take a Break Before You Break.*

The chance to go to the market or get your hair done can be a wonderful break. Time spent with another person is good for both of you.

Visit National Adult Day Services Association at **NADSA.org.**

GOLDEN RESOURCES

Low Cost Dental, Vision & Hearing Aids

Colleges and Universities can be an incredible resource for obtaining the dental services you need at a fraction of the cost, with many providing comprehensive dental care including root canals, oral surgery and dentures. Fees are generally 30–50% less than that of an established dental practice. For Donated Dental Services in your area, check through your Area Aging Council at **N4A.org**.

Free and low cost hearing aids are available through a variety of organizations. Eligibility varies; call your Area Aging Council for more details. CapTel phones are covered at no cost through OEI. There is also equipment available at no cost for people who have combined hearing and vision loss. Ask and ye shall receive! Visit **OEIUS.org**.

GOLDEN RESOURCES

Caregiver Binder Template

A three-ring binder is a wonderful way to organize information in a way that also keeps it easily accessible. You can download a free template and create your own custom binder. The template is very large, but you can choose to use the sections and pages that matter most to you. You might want to make a slimmer "Travel Binder" that can assist others who may help care for your loved one with information about medications, favorite foods, music, activities, and daily routines. Be mindful of confidential information (bank account, social security numbers) in the master binder. Having this information in one spot can save a lot of time and stress.

Get your free template at **Springwell.com**.

HELP GETTING THROUGH THE DAY

Serenity Prayer

God grant me the serenity to accept the things I cannot change;

courage to accept the things I can;

and the wisdom to know the difference.

There are some days when this reminder
is all we need to get through the day.

HELP GETTING THROUGH THE DAY

Facebook Pages & Groups

In addition to the *Caregiver Coffeebreak* and the *Caregiver Coffeebreak Club*, there are some terrific websites that have Facebook pages and Facebook groups dedicated to helping caregivers with resources, personal essays or private support groups.
Here are a few of those resources:

- **DailyCaring.com** posts helpful resources every day.

- **TheMighty.com** publishes essays and support for people facing disability, disease, and mental illness together.

- **Facebook.com/Memory-People-126017237474382/** is a private Facebook page that supports those caring for people with dementia.

- **CareGiving.com** has great resources, blogs and events for Caregivers.

- Also, don't forget to join me for your daily coffeebreak at **Facebook. com/Breeda.Miller/**

HELP GETTING THROUGH THE DAY

Daily Chuckle

Make a plan to bring a smile to your face every day and
you can call it your Daily Chuckle. You can get your
laughs through a variety of sources:

- For a free option, visit your local library. They have all sorts of videos,
funny movies, classic TV shows and stand-up comedians.

- Audio books are another great option available through your library,
or resources like **Audible.com.**

- YouTube and a number of other networks offer free streaming or
replays of popular programs.

- Subscription Services — for a small monthly fee — can give you
access to a huge number of movies and TV shows. Try **Netflix.com**,
Amazon Prime, **Hulu.com**, **PureFlix.com**, and more. You may also
pick up some great DVDs at thrift stores for a buck or two.

HELP GETTING THROUGH THE DAY

Movies and TV Shows

Build a list and ask for recommendations from friends so when you are in need of a chuckle you don't have to scroll through a long menu of options or search the shelves in the library.

Here's a start, but it's important to watch what *you* think is funny, not other family members.

Movie suggestions: Some Like it Hot, Blazing Saddles, Planes, Trains and Automobiles, Mean Girls, Pitch Perfect.

TV Shows: Modern Family, Seinfeld, Dick Van Dyke, Whose Line Is It Anyway?, Frasier, Will and Grace. What are your favorites? See more recommendations at **BreedaMiller.com/downloads.**

HELP GETTING THROUGH THE DAY

It's Not You — It's the System

The Senior Care System is far from perfect. Lower your expectations and you will reduce the amount of stress and frustration in your life as a caregiver. Most people who work for the agencies and organizations who serve the senior care community are good people who are doing the best they can with very limited resources. That said, do your best to learn what services they can actually provide and what you need to do (forms, applications, legal or medical documentation, fees) to qualify for their services.

Try to cultivate an attitude of gratitude and your tone and mindset might improve your experience with an overworked and underpaid employee at one of these service providers. Have realistic expectations and if you have a bad experience with an individual, don't give them the power to upset you. Find another route or person to talk to. Caregiving is hard enough.

HELP GETTING THROUGH THE DAY

Your One Thing

Everyday find one thing that you can enjoy, just for you.

Maybe it's having some warm tea in a nice cup. Maybe it's reading one chapter in a good novel, or taking a ten minute walk – alone. Maybe it's enjoying a nice hot shower with good smelling shampoo or a long bath with relaxing, aromatic salts.

Whatever it is, make sure you take time to enjoy this small pleasure. Be mindful, be aware, and don't rush through your few moments.

If you have to go outside on the porch to have a few minutes of peace — do it.

HELP GETTING THROUGH THE DAY

70

Respite Care

Respite Care means a short time of rest or relief.

It's a service to provide a break for the caregiver while your loved one receives care from qualified individuals. There are many different ways and settings in which respite care can be provided. Not only is respite care helpful for the caregiver, it can also be beneficial for the person receiving the care to have a break, and experience a different routine.

Download this PDF that gives explanations of different types of respite care to consider: **BreedaMiller.com/downloads.**

HELP GETTING THROUGH THE DAY

You Got to Have Friends

Bette Midler sang it best. *You got to have friends.* The feeling
of isolation is so very real in caregiving, even if
there are other people living with you.

You need to be able to connect with friends and talk about "normal
stuff," not about caregiving. This is a hard thing to actually do.
It's easy to blow off get-togethers because it takes a lot of work to
set up alternate care for your loved one. You won't be able to do
it as often and as easily as you have in the past but make the effort.
It is worth it. Even if it's for a cup of coffee for half an hour,
you will feel connected and remember what "normal life"
is like, if not once a week, at least once a month.

You don't want to lose yourself while being a caregiver.

NEEDA BREEDA – INTRODUCTION

The tips in the following *Needa Breeda* section are distilled from the many videos and blogs I have created for caregivers like you. Sometimes you need a friend to keep you company, especially when it's the middle of the night and you feel that you are the only one dealing with the challenges of caregiving. Maybe you Needa Breeda (translation: Need a Breather)! That's the time to watch a short video, listen to a story, or read a blog post.

Caregiving can be a lonely business and you can easily feel isolated and frustrated. My hope is that these stories and videos will help you out in those times and that your heart will be a bit lighter and your burden eased. When you Needa Breeda, you'll know where to find me.

BREEDAMILLER.COM

Breeda Miller

NEEDA BREEDA

Just Nearer to the Gate

My uncle was diagnosed with terminal cancer.
He was a charming man, beloved by many.

When people offered him condolences, his reply was priceless. "Aren't we all in the departure lounge? I'm just a bit nearer to the gate."

He knew his time here would soon end and he made the most of it. Perhaps we should all live each day as if we are near to the gate; we might just be.

I invite you to take a little coffee break and hear the full story on my website by visiting **BreedaMiller.com/video**.

NEEDA BREEDA

73

When a Race Isn't a Race

It's all about perspective and understanding what the goal really is.

Our son ran in his first organized sporting event — a Special Olympics Track Meet. He was thrilled to participate, wear a team jersey, and run with his friends. As we cheered from the sideline, we were shocked when he stopped in the middle of the track, immobile.

A few seconds later he began to run and at the finish line amidst the cheers and high fives we learned a valuable life lesson. Our idea of the purpose of the event and his were very different.

You can get the rest of the story from *The Moth Story Slam–Gifted*.

Check out the video here: **BreedaMiller.com/video**.

NEEDA BREEDA

74

Improv for One

Communicating with a person who has dementia can be terribly frustrating. Trying to explain things and bring them to your reality is an exercise in futility. Instead, try to enter their reality.

As long as everyone is safe, what harm does it do to play along and respond cheerfully to what is on their mind? In improvisational comedy, the rule is that one actor responds to other actors in a positive way and builds the scene. They hear a statement from one actor and they are to respond with, "Yes, and ...." so that the scene can continue.

Try to think of your interaction as an *Improv for One* session and you might be less frustrated and even entertained.
Visit **BreedaMiller.com/blog** for more!

NEEDA BREEDA

Treasured Memory

Objects in themselves can have value beyond
the price people might pay.

Objects connected to memories of people are among our most precious
possessions. This is a story about my mother's teapot collection and how
we found a way to help her adjust to her new surroundings in our home
and keep her treasures safe. It might be just a teapot to others, but to
my mom, her teapots represented her family and her heritage.

Join me for the story here (entitled Labor of Love),
at **BreedaMiller.com/blog**.

NEEDA BREEDA

76

Deception

Deceiving a parent is not often considered a kindness, but when
dealing with dementia and anxiety about the end of life,
it can be the greatest gift of all.

I myself had to delve into some therapeutic fibbing when my mother
was near the end of her life. She was filled with so much anxiety
about her impending "journey," but thankfully, I was finally
able to truly listen and hear what she needed.

Of all places, I found the inspiration I needed in a Google search.
I was able to ease her worry, put a smile on her
face, and we both had a good laugh.

Check out the whole story on my website here:
BreedaMiller.com/video.

BONUS:

BREEDA'S CAREGIVER AFFIRMATION

(with appropriate hand gestures, facial expressions and emphasis)

I am a caregiver (matter of fact statement).

I am compassionate (hand over heart).

I am courageous (hands on hips, head to the side, with attitude).

I am resilient (lean back and bounce forward carefully).

I care for myself (hug yourself).

I CAN DO THIS (fist pump).

For

I AM a CAREGIVER (hands over head, victory signs).

(whisper crowd roar)

Check out the video (with choreography) at **BreedaMiller.com/video**.

A NOTE FROM BREEDA

I hope you've enjoyed the tips in this book. If you'd like more ideas, stories and support be sure to check out the Caregiver Coffeebreak videos on my website, **BreedaMiller.com**.

Just as every person is a unique individual, every caregiver has their own style of caring and every person receiving care has their own needs and desires. Not every idea works in every situation, but successful (and sane) caregivers keep trying new and creative ideas to solve problems and provide care with dignity and grace.

My hope is that I have provided a bit of comfort for you, like sitting at the kitchen table enjoying a cuppa something warm and comforting with a good friend.

Breeda Miller

ABOUT BREEDA MILLER

Breeda Miller has spent the better part of the last 10 years as the caregiver of her dear mother, up to and including hospice care in her home. In dealing with dementia, incontinence and insomnia, every day was a new adventure. Add in raising kids and working full time; it was a hoot. In between doling out medicine and cleaning up more bodily fluids than one should ever discuss, Breeda found that humor helped her cope.

She now speaks to organizations about *Caring for the Caregiver* and about *Finding Humor and Grace in the Caregiver Sandwich*. She is an award-winning story teller and has appeared nationally on the *Moth Story Hour* on NPR. She is married to the most patient man on Earth and has three great kids who survived an often cranky and exhausted caregiving mother.

THE CAREGIVER COFFEEBREAK CLUB

Breeda Miller's Caregiver Coffeebreak Club is a membership group that provides access to additional resources for professional and family caregivers through a private online support community, video "helpinars" and interviews with relevant professionals.

You can find out more at **BreedaMiller.com**.

CALMING COLORING JOURNAL FOR CAREGIVERS

By Breeda Miller

Both journaling and coloring have proven to help alleviate stress.

Here's a perfect combination you can keep in your bag! Take it with you to doctor appointments, and you can color and doodle while you wait. There are also full pages for journaling so you can take notes during the visit.

The best part is that you can make it your own. It could become a gratitude journal, a record of funny stories, or it may simply be a place where you can express yourself freely — frustrations and all.

Order your copy today at
BreedaMiller.com/CaregiverCoffeebreak.

THE CAREGIVER COLORING JOURNAL

CAREGIVER COFFEEBREAK STRESS CUP

A fun caregiver gift is this squeezable cup of coffee to have on hand for those moments when you just need to relieve some tension. For details on how to get one, visit **BreedaMiller.com/CaregiverCoffeebreak**.

CAREGIVER CARE PACK

Brighten the day of a caregiver you know
with a gift bag that contains:

- The Caregiver Coffeebreak Tip Book

- A Caregiver Coloring Journal

- A petite six-pack of coloring pencils

- A Caregiver Stress Cup

- A scented bath treat

BREEDA MILLER SPEAKING

Breeda Miller Speaking provides keynotes and breakout sessions for organizations desiring to support professional and/or family caregivers.

Breeda also presents to groups needing a positive message of self-care entitled "Take a Break Before You Break." Her intelligent wit, life experiences, and engaging content are ideal for:

- Organizations looking to support professional caregivers to help find ways to reduce employee burnout and turnover

- Support groups for family caregivers

- Forward thinking companies who seek to offer stress management programs for employees

- Parents of special needs children

- Retreats—a humorous way to address delicate issues

- Staff enrichment programs

For more information, please go to **BreedaMiller.com/Speaking**, or send an email to **Breeda@BreedaMiller.com**.

CONNECT WITH BREEDA MILLER:

BreedaMiller.com

CaregiverCoffeebreak.com

Breeda@BreedaMiller.com

FIND BREEDA ON SOCIAL MEDIA:

Facebook.com/Breeda.Miller

LinkedIn.com/in/BreedaMiller

Twitter.com/BreedaMiller

YouTube.com/Breeda Miller

Hashtag: #NeedaBreeda

PARTING THOUGHTS

On any given day you can only do the best you are able to do. If you are mentally, physically and emotionally exhausted, you will not have the stamina to provide the level of care you want to give.

Caregiving is like a river — you can never step in the same one twice. No two days are the same. What works one day may have no impact the next. The idea is to keep trying new ideas and resources to help your caregiving situation while at the same time finding ways to care for yourself.

Don't give up. Regroup. Take it one day at a time. Find support and most importantly, *Take a Break Before You Break*.

Breeda Miller